Contents

LB BOOKS

Published 2022. Little Brother Books Ltd, Ground Floor,
23 Southernhay East, Exeter, Devon EX1 1QL
books@littlebrotherbooks.co.uk | www.littlebrotherbooks.co.uk
Printed in the United Kingdom
The Little Brother Books trademark, email and website addresses,
are the sole and exclusive properties of Little Brother Books Limited.

ONLINE ACTIVITIES

SCAN CODE

On some of the pages you will see QR codes. These QR codes take you to online Purple Mash activities which support learning from the relevant page.

To use the QR codes, scan the QR code with the camera on your web enabled tablet, click on the link and the activity will appear on screen.

Alternatively, QR readers are available on the app store for your device.

purple mash

Numbers to 100

Hoppin' clams, SpongeBob needs to keep count of the number of jellyfish he and Patrick have caught. Can you help him count to 100?

1

Count from **1** to **100** using the hundred square, and where there is a number missing, write it in.

1	2	3	4	5	6	7	8		10
	12	13		15		17	18	19	
21	22	23	24	25	26		28	29	30
31		33	34		36	37	38	39	
41	42	43		45	46	47		49	50
51	52	53	54	55		57	58		60
61	62	63		65	66	67		69	70
71		73	74	75	76		78	79	
81	82	83	84	85	86	87	88	89	90
91	92	93		95	96	97	98		100

2

Patrick has cut up the hundred square and wants you to fill in the missing numbers. Count along and write in what is missing. You can use the hundred square above to help if you need it.

a.

17	18		
27		29	
	38	39	40
		49	50

b.

31			34
		43	
51		53	
	62		

c.

	54		56
		65	
	74		
	84		
93			

Counting

Greedy Mr. Krabs wants to know if he's made more money than the Chum Bucket, so counting carefully is very important.

1

Mr. Krabs wants to count the food SpongeBob serves up at the Krusty Krab. Can you help him write the numbers?

a.

b.

c.

d.

Write the words to match the digits.

11 ....

4 ....

8 ....

19 ....

2

Patrick is helping SpongeBob count burgers. Can you help him match the pile of burgers to the numbers? Count the burgers and then draw a line to the number you have counted.

a.

b.

c.

d.

e.

f.

20

7

2

14

11

5

Counting

SpongeBob is busy cooking in the Krusty Krab kitchen. He's got lots of orders to make!

1

Help SpongeBob by looking at the different amounts and drawing the correct number of food items.

 a. 8 Krabby Patty burgers

 b. 5 pizzas

 c. 3 Kelp Shakes

 d. 4 Krusty Dogs

2

SpongeBob knows that counting in order is very important! Can you join the dots? What is the hidden picture?

One More & One Less

It's a busy day at the Krusty Krab and everyone is ordering lots of food. Unfortunately, some of the customers keep changing their minds and altering their orders by adding things or taking them off. Can you help SpongeBob sort the orders out?

1

Count the number of food types and write down one more and one less than the number shown in the pictures. The first one has been done for you.

		One more	One less
a.		7	5
b.			
c.			
d.			

2

SpongeBob is having to match receipts to the customers. Match each sentence to the correct answer.

a. 1 more than 5 is	0
b. 1 less than 12 is	11
c. 1 more than 19 is	15
d. 1 less than 1 is	6
e. 1 more than 14 is	20

Comparing Numbers

Much to the annoyance of Squidward, SpongeBob has built a bubble blowing machine and is charging everyone 25 cents to blow a bubble. Even though Patrick isn't as good as SpongeBob, he has found he has a talent for blowing amazing elephant shaped bubbles!

1

Look at the numbers and write them in the bubbles in order from smallest to largest.

| 1 | 11 | 21 | 4 | 19 | 8 |

2

SpongeBob and Patrick have been comparing the bubbles they have blown. They use symbols to help.

< means less than   > means greater than   = means same as

Remember, the arrow always points to the smaller number. For example, 4 < 5

a. 14 ☐ 10

b. 17 ☐ 17

c. 3 ☐ 9

d. 8 ☐ 16

e. 20 ☐ 3

Value of Digits

Sheldon Plankton, the owner of rival restaurant Chum Bucket, is determined to steal Mr. Krabs secret formula for Krabby Patties and spends his life planning different ways to do this. Plankton thinks he has finally found part of the secret formula but needs help working out the numbers next to the ingredients.

	tens	ones
25=	2	5

20 + 5

The number 25 is made up of 2 tens and 5 ones.

1

How many tens and ones are in these numbers?

a. 65 = ☐ tens and ☐ ones

b. 42 = ☐ tens and ☐ ones

c. 38 = ☐ tens and ☐ ones

d. 13 = ☐ tens and ☐ ones

e. 26 = ☐ tens and ☐ ones

2

What number do these tens and ones make?

a. 3 tens and 2 ones = ☐

b. 7 tens and 5 ones = ☐

c. 4 tens and 9 ones = ☐

d. 5 tens and 1 one = ☐

e. 1 ten and 7 ones = ☐

3

The digits in these numbers represent tens and ones. Add these numbers together and write the new number. The first one has been done for you.

a. 30 shrimps + 4 shrimps = 34 shrimps

b. 10 kelp leaves + 7 kelp leaves = ☐ kelp leaves

c. 20 sea cheeses + 5 sea cheeses = ☐ sea cheeses

d. 40 sea onions + 9 sea onions = ☐ sea onions

Solving Number Problems

On one of their regular visits, SpongeBob and Patrick notice that the popcorn boxes are being counted at the Reef Cinema. They are packed in big boxes of 10 with some single popcorn boxes as well.

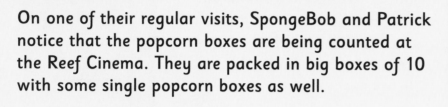

10 + 10 + 3 = 23 boxes of popcorn

1 Write down the number of popcorn boxes there are in each image below.

a. 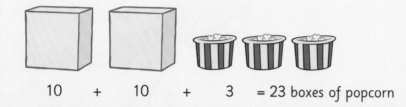 □

b. □

c. □

d. □

2 Which of Patrick's statements are correct? Tick true or false for each one.

	True	False
a. 4 big boxes and 3 small ones make 43 popcorn boxes.	□	□
b. 54 is bigger than 6 tens and 1 one.	□	□
c. 20 is the same as 1 ten and 2 ones.	□	□
d. 10 tens can be written as 100.	□	□
e. Five more than 85 is 91.	□	□

Adding & Taking Away to 10

SpongeBob is adding to his bubble blowing record! He can blow lots of bubbles very quickly. He's trying to see how many bubbles he can blow before they start to pop.

1

Work out how many bubbles SpongeBob has managed to blow. Draw the bubbles to help you.

4 bubbles + 1 bubbles = 5 bubbles

a. 6 + 2 =

b. 7 + 3 =

c. 5 + 3 =

2

SpongeBob's bubbles have hidden some of the numbers. Find the numbers in these sums hidden by the bubbles to make these questions correct.

a. 3 + ⬜ = 5   b. ⬜ + 1 = 10   c. 5 + ⬜ = 9   d. ⬜ + 3 = 7

3

Every time a bubble pops, one is subtracted, or taken away, from Spongebob's total.

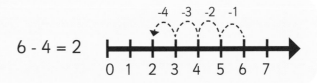

6 - 4 = 2

Answer the questions below by counting backwards along the number line.

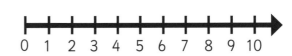

a. 7 - 4 = ⬜   b. 9 - 2 = ⬜   c. 4 - 2 = ⬜   d. 7 - 3 = ⬜

Adding & Taking Away to 20

Squidward is working on the till at the Krusty Krab, but Plankton has unplugged the power! Squidward is struggling to add up customers bills and his brain is beginning to hurt. Mr. Krabs is getting mad with Squidward as he is going very slowly!

1

Can you help Squidward to calculate the bills? Use the number line to help you.

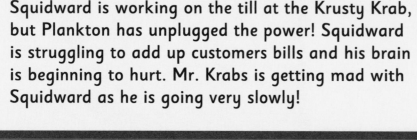

0 1 2 3 4 5 6 7 8 9 10 11 12 13 14 15 16 17 18 19 20

a. 13 + 6 = ☐

b. 8 + 7 = ☐

c. 14 + 2 = ☐

d. 9 + 3 = ☐

e. 7 - 6 = ☐

f. 15 - 5 = ☐

g. 12 - 7 = ☐

h. 19 - 10 = ☐

2

A big group has come into the diner which means the bills are even larger. Number bonds to 10 can help us answer questions with larger numbers.

8 + 2 = 10 **so** 80 + 20 = 100

Use this method to fill in the gaps and work out the missing numbers.

a. 6 + ☐ = 10 **so** 60 + ☐ = 100

b. ☐ + 8 = 10 **so** ☐ + 80 = 100

c. ☐ + 3 = 10 **so** ☐ + 30 = 100

d. 5 + ☐ = 10 **so** 50 + ☐ = 100

e. ☐ + 9 = 10 **so** ☐ + 90 = 100

Addition & Subtraction

SpongeBob and Patrick LOVE to catch jellyfish! The two friends have been to Jellyfish Fields on the edge of Bikini Bottom to see how many jellyfish they can catch. They are adding together their catches to work out the total number collected.

    +    4 + 3 = 7

1

Join a line to match the number of jellyfish both friends caught with the correct total number.

a.
     9

b.
          12

c.
             10

d.
             11

2

Some of the jellyfish have escaped from the jar!
Work out how many are left now.

         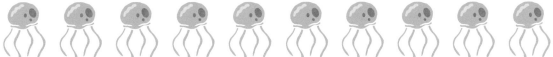

a. 10 - 7 = ☐   **b.** 10 - 4 = ☐   **c.** 9 - 5 = ☐   **d.** 8 - 6 = ☐

Addition & Subtraction

Some of the bills at the Krusty Krab have accidentally been covered in sauce so Squidward can't see all the numbers! Use the number square to help him work out which numbers are missing from the sums below.

1	2	3	4	5	6	7	8	9	10
11	12	13	14	15	16	17	18	19	20
21	22	23	24	25	26	27	28	29	30
31	32	33	34	35	36	37	38	39	40
41	42	43	44	45	46	47	48	49	50
51	52	53	54	55	56	57	58	59	60
61	62	63	64	65	66	67	68	69	70
71	72	73	74	75	76	77	78	79	80
81	82	83	84	85	86	87	88	89	90
91	92	93	94	95	96	97	98	99	100

1

21 + = 43. To find the missing number, you could count how many jumps it is from 21 to 43.

It takes 22 jumps from 21 to land on 43. So, 21 + **22** = 43

These number sentences use adding.

a. 10 + ⬡ = 19

b. ⬡ + 21 = 46

c. 17 + ⬡ = 32

d. ⬡ + 12 = 20

e. 34 + ⬡ = 43

f. 21 + ⬡ = 52

2

30 – ⬡ = 12. To find the missing number, you could count how many jumps back it is from 30 to 12.

It takes 18 jumps back from 30 to land on 12. So, 30 – **18** = 12

These number sentences use take away.

a. 27 – ⬡ = 15

b. 48 – ⬡ = 36

c. 37 – ⬡ = 29

d. 14 – ⬡ = 7

e. 22 – ⬡ = 18

f. ⬡ – 13 = 21

Addition & Subtraction

The Flying Dutchman has made a series of challenges to stop SpongeBob getting home. Can you help him to solve them?

1

Complete the number sentences to help SpongeBob get home.

a. 14 + 3 = ☐

b. 9 + 9 = ☐

c. 15 + 4 = ☐

d. 12 + 7 = ☐

e. 17 + 6 = ☐

f. 26 + 30 = ☐

g. 35 + 20 = ☐

h. 12 + 50 = ☐

i. 23 + 40 = ☐

j. 36 + 10 = ☐

Part Whole Models

Help! SpongeBob has lost some of Mrs. Puff's Good Noodle star stickers which he was given for excellent behaviour at Boating School. He is searching for them but can't remember how many he needs to look for!

1 Can you help Spongebob by filling in the missing numbers?

These are part whole models; the whole is at the top and it is split into 2 parts.

a.
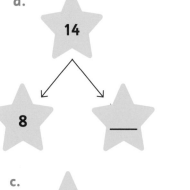
14
8 ___

b.
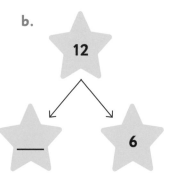
12
___ 6

11
5 6

c.
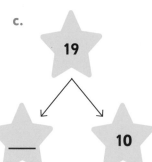
19
___ 10

d.
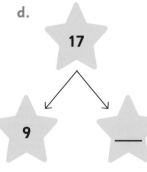
17
9 ___

RULES of the ROAD

2 SpongeBob was awarded 11 Good Noodle stars and the next day, another 8. How many Good Noodle stars did he get altogether?

3 SpongeBob was awarded 13 Good Noodle stars, but then crashed and Mrs. Puff took away 5. How many were left?

4 SpongeBob already had 9 Good Noodle stars and Mrs. Puff gave him 9 more stars for following the rules of the road. How many did he have in total?

Finding the Inverse

Sandy Cheeks is a thrill seeker who loves nothing better than extreme sports and karate. She realises that as well as working her body, she needs to work out her brain. To do this, she's been solving some maths problems as quickly as she can.

Sandy realises that if you know that $4 + 5 = 9$ then it takes no time at all to work out that $5 + 4 = 9$. She can quickly swap the numbers over to work out subtraction questions too so $9 - 5 = 4$ and $9 - 4 = 5$.

1

Use these number facts to fill in the missing answers.

a. $3 + 6 = 9$ so $9 - 6 = \boxed{}$

b. $10 + 5 = 15$ so $15 - \boxed{} = 10$

c. $20 - 8 = 12$ so $8 + \boxed{} = 20$

d. $13 + 3 = 16$ so $16 - 3 = \boxed{}$

e. $14 - 5 = 9$ so $\boxed{} + 9 = 14$

2

Have a go at writing the number sentences about these fact families.

a. 12   4   16

___ + ___ = ___   ___ + ___ = ___   ___ – ___ = ___   ___ – ___ = ___

b. 10   7   17

___ + ___ = ___   ___ + ___ = ___   ___ – ___ = ___   ___ – ___ = ___

c. 14   6   20

___ + ___ = ___   ___ + ___ = ___   ___ – ___ = ___   ___ – ___ = ___

Grouping & Arrays

Patrick, SpongeBob and Squidward are blowing bubbles again! Patrick and Squidward just can't get bubble sizes like SpongeBob can, so SpongeBob is showing them how. SpongeBob wants to work out the total amount of bubbles blown on each attempt by grouping them together.

1

We count in groups when we multiply, and Squidward and Patrick are blowing multiple bubbles! Work out the total number of bubbles below.

a. 3 groups of 3 = ☐

b. 2 groups of 5 = ☐

c. 4 groups of 2 = ☐

d. 5 groups of 4 = ☐

e. 2 groups of 10 = ☐

2

Mr. Krabs is obsessed with money and has persuaded SpongeBob to charge Squidward and Patrick for teaching them to blow bubbles. He uses arrays to help him multiply. Try these:

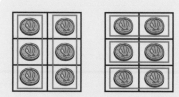

Mr. Krab could interpret these arrays as 2 groups of 3 coins (2 x 3) or 3 groups of 2 coins (3 x 2). Both arrays show a total of 6 coins.

a. 2 x 4 = ☐
4 x 2 = ☐

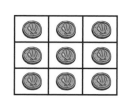

b. 3 x 3 = ☐

c. 2 x 7 = ☐
7 x 2 = ☐

d. 5 x 2 = ☐
2 x 5 = ☐

2s, 5s & 10s

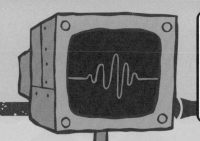

As part of their plan for world domination, Plankton and Karen have created a multiplication machine in the kitchen of the Chum Bucket.

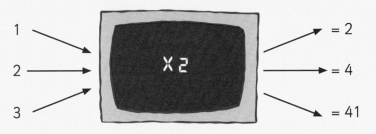

1 → X2 → = 2

2 → = 4

3 → = 41

1 Complete the machine's numbers. The first one has been done for you.

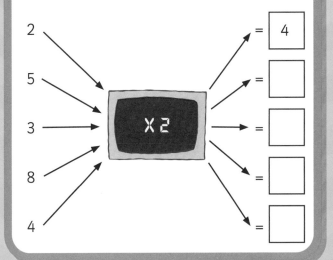

2 → X2 → = 4

5 → =

3 → =

8 → =

4 → =

2 Karen has worked some super-computer magic and changed what the machine multiplies by. Complete the numbers.

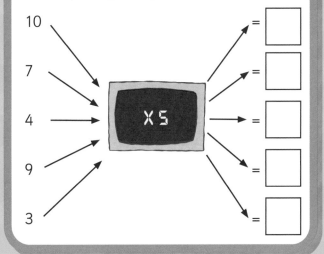

10 → X5 → =

7 → =

4 → =

9 → =

3 → =

3 Plankton has set the machine to multiply by 10 but now it's working on maximum power, it's starting to make mistakes! Fix the wrong answers by writing the correct numbers in the boxes.

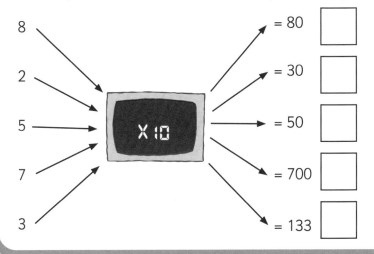

8 → X10 → = 80

2 → = 30

5 → = 50

7 → = 700

3 → = 133

Odds & Evens

Gary has slid into Bikini Bottom School and slithered slime all over the odd and even maths number lines that Squidward created when he attended school ... a very long time ago! The children still use them to work out which numbers are odd, and which are even.

1

Complete these number lines with odd and even numbers.

a.

2   6   8   12   18

b.

3   7   9   15   19

2

Are all of these numbers in the right box? Circle any that are incorrect.

ODD

15   6   5
1   3   17   5
7   1   12

EVEN

1   6   4   8
2   11   7   10

3

Use your knowledge of odd and even numbers to join the dots to reveal each picture.

Odd numbers

Even numbers

Multiplying & Dividing

Mr. Krabs is using multiplication and division to work out how many burgers he has been selling each day. He knows how closely related multiplication and division are.

1

Match each multiplication number sentence with the correct diagram and division number sentence. The first one has been done for you.

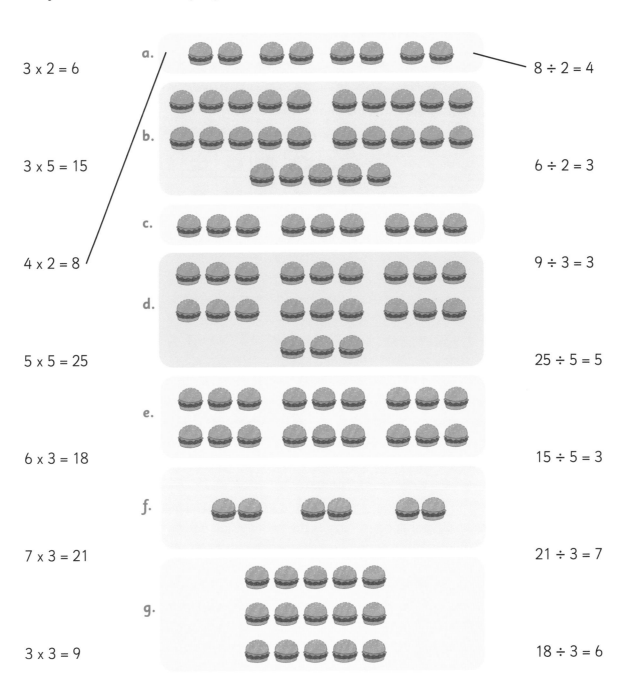

3 x 2 = 6

a.

8 ÷ 2 = 4

3 x 5 = 15

b.

6 ÷ 2 = 3

c.

4 x 2 = 8

9 ÷ 3 = 3

d.

5 x 5 = 25

25 ÷ 5 = 5

e.

6 x 3 = 18

15 ÷ 5 = 3

f.

7 x 3 = 21

21 ÷ 3 = 7

g.

3 x 3 = 9

18 ÷ 3 = 6

Multiplying & Dividing

SpongeBob knows that you can flip a Krabby Patty two ways to get the same result, and that works with multiplication and division too!

An array is an arrangement of rows and columns that match a multiplication. We can write multiplication and division facts for them like the example here:

2 x 4 = 8

4 x 2 = 8

8 ÷ 2 = 4

8 ÷ 4 = 2

1

Write the multiplication and division facts for these arrays of burgers.

a.

_____ x _____ = _____

_____ x _____ = _____

_____ ÷ _____ = _____

_____ ÷ _____ = _____

c.

_____ x _____ = _____   _____ ÷ _____ = _____

_____ x _____ = _____   _____ ÷ _____ = _____

b.

_____ x _____ = _____

_____ x _____ = _____

_____ ÷ _____ = _____

_____ ÷ _____ = _____

2

Division needs to be done in a more careful order, just like SpongeBob needs to be careful around Mr. Krabs! Look at each array and decide which of the two division number sentences underneath it could be correct. Circle your answer.

a.

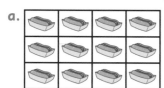

12 ÷ 3 = 4

4 ÷ 4 = 16

b.

1 ÷ 3 = 1

3 ÷ 1 = 3

c.

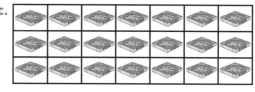

21 ÷ 7 = 3

3 ÷ 24 = 8

Multiplication Problems

Larry the Lobster is the best lifeguard in Bikini Bottom. Sometimes, he rescues the Bottomites before they even realise that they are in difficulty! Can you solve these problems faster than Larry can save a swimmer in need?

1

Using your 2, 5 and 10 times tables, answer these questions.

a. 5 x 3 = ☐   **b.** 10 x 10 = ☐   **c.** 8 x 5 = ☐   **d.** 2 x 1 = ☐

e. 7 x 2 = ☐   **f.** 3 x 2 = ☐   **g.** 9 x 10 = ☐   **h.** 5 x 5 = ☐

2

Karen Plankton has told Larry that he can be even faster with his rescues if he saves multiple Bottomites at once using multiplication instead of adding repeatedly.

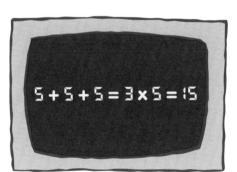

$5 + 5 + 5 = 3 \times 5 = 15$

Turn these repeated addition number sentences into multiplication to show how much faster he could be!

a. 3 + 3 + 3 = 9

☐ x ☐ = ☐

b. 4 + 4 = 8

☐ x ☐ = ☐

c. 10 + 10 + 10 + 10 = 40

☐ x ☐ = ☐

d. 2 + 2 + 2 + 2 + 2 = 10

☐ x ☐ = ☐

3

a. Larry goes to the beach for 10 minutes a day for 3 days.
How many minutes does he spend at the beach altogether?

b. Larry the Lobster has 5 groups of 8 adoring fans.
How many fans have come to see him? ☐

c. Larry has 9 pairs of dumbbells in the gym.
How many does it have altogether? ☐

21

Division Problems

Patrick is a good friend and likes to divide everything he has with SpongeBob. He has made eight Patty Pals as he knows SpongeBob loves these and he wants to share half with him.

So, eight divided between Patrick and SpongeBob means they get four each (8 ÷ 2 = 4).

1

Use your number facts to solve these division questions.

a. 8 ÷ 2 =

b. 35 ÷ 5 =

c. 12 ÷ 2 =

d. 10 ÷ 5 =

e. 100 ÷ 10 =

f. 20 ÷ 5 =

g. 50 ÷ 10 =

h. 18 ÷ 2 =

i. 30 ÷ 10 =

2

Patrick and SpongeBob are sharing a pile of 10 Krabby Patties.

How many do they each have?

3

SpongeBob splits his catch of 20 jellyfish into 4 jars.

How many are in each jar?

4

Mr. Krabs needs 50 rolls for the hot dogs. The rolls come in bags of 5.

How many bags does he need to buy?

5

Squidward grew 50 vegetables in his garden and put them into 10 boxes.

How many vegetables were in each box?

Finding a Half

SpongeBob and Patrick have gone on a picnic to the boardwalk and are sharing their food! They need to split everything in half, this means two equal parts, so that it is fair, and they both get the same.

We can write a half like this: $\frac{1}{2}$

1

Find which of these strawberries is cut in half and draw a circle around it. Remember that a half is 2 equal parts.

2

Patrick is trying to cut this Krabby Patty in half to share. Can you help him? Draw a line through the burger to cut it into 2 equal parts.

3

SpongeBob knows that he can share things out into 2 equal piles to find half of an amount. He has bought some popcorn to share with Patrick.

While he is busy on the Boardwalk Coaster, can you find a half of these popcorn amounts?

a. $\frac{1}{2}$ of 4 = ☐   b. $\frac{1}{2}$ of 10 = ☐   c. $\frac{1}{2}$ of 6 = ☐   d. $\frac{1}{2}$ of 12 = ☐

Finding a Quarter

SpongeBob is having a birthday party and his friends have come to celebrate with him! There are four of them so everything needs to be split into four equal parts.

These are called quarters and we can write a quarter like this: $\frac{1}{4}$

1

Which of these birthday cakes is cut into quarters? Draw a circle around it.

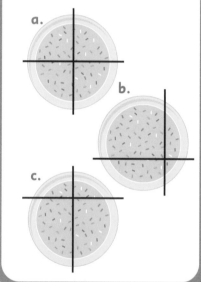

a.

b.

c.

2

SpongeBob wants to share doughnuts between himself and his three friends at the party. Colour in a quarter of the doughnuts.

3

SpongeBob knows that to share out the cakes into quarters, he needs to split them into 4 equal groups. While he is playing party games, have a go at finding a quarter of these amounts to see how many cakes each person will get.

a. $\frac{1}{4}$ of 8 = ☐   b. $\frac{1}{4}$ of 16 = ☐   c. $\frac{1}{4}$ of 4 = ☐   d. $\frac{1}{4}$ of 12 = ☐

Fractions of Shapes

Fractions are parts of a whole. When we write fractions, we think about how many parts the whole has been split in to.

Sandy Cheeks has been playing football and knows the football pitch is split into 2 halves.

We can write a half as: $\frac{1}{2}$

1

The pitch has been divided into two halves. Colour in one half.

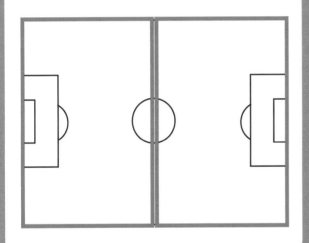

2

Sandy also likes to swim, and the pool is split into 4 equal parts. These are called quarters. We can write a quarter as $\frac{1}{4}$.

Colour in $\frac{1}{4}$ of the swimming pool.

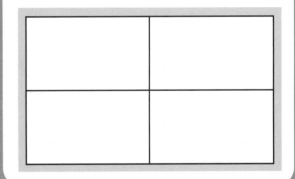

3

Sandy really likes playing netball, and the court is split into 3 equal parts, called thirds.

Colour in $\frac{1}{3}$ of the netball court.

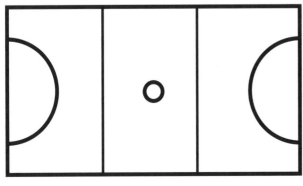

Fractions of Amounts

SpongeBob and Patrick love going fishing at Jellyfish Fields. They always share their catch between all of their friends, so everyone can make jellyfish jam for their sandwiches.

1

Circle the correct number of jellyfish for each of the fractions below and write the answers in the boxes. The first one has been done for you.

a. $\frac{1}{2}$ of 10 = 5

b. $\frac{1}{4}$ of 8 = ☐

c. $\frac{2}{4}$ of 8 = ☐

d. $\frac{3}{4}$ of 8 = ☐

e. $\frac{1}{2}$ of 4 = ☐

f. $\frac{1}{4}$ of 4 = ☐

g. $\frac{2}{4}$ of 4 = ☐

2

Every time SpongeBob and Patrick go to the Bi-Annual Jellyfish Convention, they can only go to a fraction of the events. Find the correct fraction of each of these number of events.

a. $\frac{1}{2}$ of 6 = ☐

b. $\frac{1}{4}$ of 20 = ☐

c. $\frac{1}{3}$ of 12 = ☐

d. $\frac{1}{2}$ of 16 = ☐

e. $\frac{1}{4}$ of 8 = ☐

f. $\frac{1}{3}$ of 18 = ☐

Equivalent Fractions

Mrs. Puff, SpongeBob's boating teacher, always has different amounts of children in her class as not all of them show up every day. Today, only half of her students are present.

Half can be written in lots of different ways.
$\frac{1}{2}$ is the same as $\frac{2}{4}$ and $\frac{4}{8}$

1 Colour half of these shapes and write the equivalent fraction.

 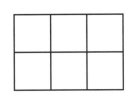

a. $\frac{1}{2} = \frac{\square}{4}$ b. $\frac{1}{2} = \frac{\square}{6}$

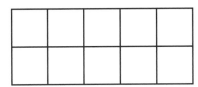

c. $\frac{1}{2} = \frac{\square}{10}$

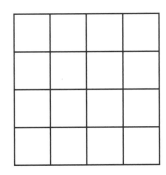

d. $\frac{1}{2} = \frac{\square}{16}$

2 On a very quiet day, Mrs. Puff only has $\frac{1}{4}$ of the seats of her classroom filled.

Draw a circle around the shapes that have $\frac{1}{4}$ coloured in.

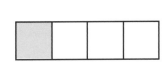 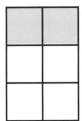

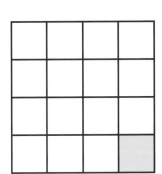

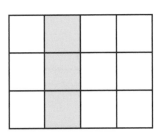

Equivalent Fractions

Plankton is wracking his brain trying to figure out why everyone seem to prefer Krusty Krab to the Chum Bucket! He has been studying the Krabby Patty and trying to find the equivalent fractions of each ingredient so he can copy it in his Chum Burger.

1

Use the fraction wall to find the equivalent fractions.

a. $\dfrac{1}{2} = \dfrac{\square}{4}$

b. $\dfrac{2}{5} = \dfrac{\square}{10}$

c. $\dfrac{3}{6} = \dfrac{\square}{2}$

d. $\dfrac{3}{4} = \dfrac{\square}{8}$

e. $\dfrac{1}{3} = \dfrac{\square}{6}$

f. $\dfrac{2}{8} = \dfrac{\square}{4}$

1 whole											
$\frac{1}{2}$						$\frac{1}{2}$					
$\frac{1}{3}$				$\frac{1}{3}$				$\frac{1}{3}$			
$\frac{1}{4}$			$\frac{1}{4}$			$\frac{1}{4}$			$\frac{1}{4}$		
$\frac{1}{5}$		$\frac{1}{5}$		$\frac{1}{5}$		$\frac{1}{5}$			$\frac{1}{5}$		
$\frac{1}{6}$		$\frac{1}{6}$		$\frac{1}{6}$		$\frac{1}{6}$		$\frac{1}{6}$		$\frac{1}{6}$	
$\frac{1}{8}$	$\frac{1}{8}$	$\frac{1}{8}$	$\frac{1}{8}$	$\frac{1}{8}$	$\frac{1}{8}$	$\frac{1}{8}$	$\frac{1}{8}$				
$\frac{1}{10}$	$\frac{1}{10}$	$\frac{1}{10}$	$\frac{1}{10}$	$\frac{1}{10}$	$\frac{1}{10}$	$\frac{1}{10}$	$\frac{1}{10}$	$\frac{1}{10}$	$\frac{1}{10}$		
$\frac{1}{12}$	$\frac{1}{12}$	$\frac{1}{12}$	$\frac{1}{12}$	$\frac{1}{12}$	$\frac{1}{12}$	$\frac{1}{12}$	$\frac{1}{12}$	$\frac{1}{12}$	$\frac{1}{12}$	$\frac{1}{12}$	$\frac{1}{12}$

2

Plankton thinks he might have managed to match the ingredients! Draw a line to match the fractions that are the same.

a. $\dfrac{1}{2}$ $\qquad$ $\dfrac{4}{6}$

b. $\dfrac{2}{3}$ $\qquad$ $\dfrac{4}{10}$

c. $\dfrac{2}{5}$ $\qquad$ $\dfrac{3}{12}$

d. $\dfrac{1}{4}$ $\qquad$ $\dfrac{4}{8}$

3

Plankton carried out a customer survey, but he is having difficulty understanding the results. Use what you know about equivalent fractions to help him by colouring in the correct answers.

a. 6 out of 12 people said they prefer Salty Sea Dogs to Chum Sticks. The fraction who prefer Chum Sticks is:

$\boxed{\dfrac{1}{2}}$ $\boxed{\dfrac{1}{3}}$ $\boxed{\dfrac{1}{4}}$

b. 3 out of 12 people said they would never return to the Chum Bucket. The fraction who would never return is:

$\boxed{\dfrac{1}{2}}$ $\boxed{\dfrac{1}{3}}$ $\boxed{\dfrac{1}{4}}$

c. 6 out of 8 people said they were ill after eating a Chum Burger. The fraction who were ill is:

$\boxed{\dfrac{1}{2}}$ $\boxed{\dfrac{1}{3}}$ $\boxed{\dfrac{1}{4}}$ $\boxed{\dfrac{3}{4}}$

Measuring

Mr. Krabs wants the Krusty Krab to make as much money as possible, so he's taking a good look at the food his restaurant serves. Can you help him by answering the questions below?

1

Label the Salty Sea Dogs to show which is **longer** and which is **shorter**.

a. _____   b. _____

2

Label the Kelp Shakes to say which is **taller** and which is **shorter**.

a. _____   b. _____

3

Label these Krabby Patties to say which is **heavier** and which is **lighter**.

a. _____   b. _____

Comparing Measurements

Mr. Krabs is wondering if he should start selling candy bars at Krusty Krab and wants to check which bar is bigger and better.

He needs to measure the length of the bars in centimetres (we can write it as cm). Help Mr. Krabs by reading the length from the ruler and writing it down.

1

KELP BAR

The Kelp Bar is _____ cm long.

0 1 2 3 4 5 6 7 8 9 10 11 12 13 14 15 16 17 18 19 20

2

KANDY

The Kandy Bar is _____ cm long.

0 1 2 3 4 5 6 7 8 9 10 11 12 13 14 15 16 17 18 19 20

3

Which is longer, the Kelp Bar or the Kandy Bar? _____

4

Mr. Krabs is also comparing the weight of his Krabby Patty against the Chum Burger served at the Chum Bucket. Read the weighing scales and write down how much each burger weighs. We are using grams and the symbol for this is g.

The Krabby Patty weighs _____ g.

The Chum Burger weighs _____ g.

Krabby Patty   Chum Burger

Plankton thinks the Chum Burger is heavier, is he right?   YES    NO

Money Values

As we know, Eugene Krabs loves nothing more than counting his money. The more he has, the happier he is. He realises that 100 pennies make a pound. Sometimes we call pennies pence.

We can write this with symbols too. 100p = £1

Hello, I like money

1

Mr. Krabs is finding different ways to make the same amounts of money. Match the pairs of amounts that make the same total. One has been done for you.

1.

2.

3.

4.

a.

b.

c.

d.

2

Mr. Krabs needs to find out how much customers need to pay for their meals, but he is very busy and needs some help.

a.		b.		c.	
Krabby Patty	50p	Pizza	30p	Hot dog	15p
Milkshake	20p	Ice cream	40p	Pizza	30p
Hot dog	15p			Krabby Patty	50p

Total _____

Total _____

Total _____

Ordering Events in a Day

Uh oh, SpongeBob has overslept and he's now late for his boating lesson with Mrs. Puff! He needs some help to get ready in record time.

1

Number the pictures to show the order of SpongeBob's morning events.

1. He is woken up by his alarm.

2. He opens his eyes and switches off the alarm.

3. He leaps out of bed with a smile.

4. He has a wash.

5. He puts on fresh square pants.

6. He loads up his toothbrush.

7. He is ready for the day!

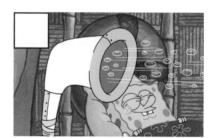

2

What time of day does SpongeBob do these things? Match the activity to the time of day.

a. Wake up   Evening

b. Go to sleep   Afternoon

c. Go jelly fishing with Patrick   Morning

Days of the Week

Patrick sometimes forgets the order of the days of the week and gets confused about when he is meeting SpongeBob. He often turns up on the wrong day!

Patrick is trying to remember that the days of the week always go in the same order:

Monday
Tuesday
Wednesday
Thursday
Friday
Saturday
Sunday

These two days are called the weekend.

1

Find the days of the week in this wordsearch.

d	a	y	a	t	h	u	r	s	d	a	y	m	d	y
s	u	n	s	u	n	d	e	r	m	o	d	f	r	i
p	e	t	n	e	r	t	e	o	o	g	h	z	c	a
o	g	o	l	s	x	w	e	d	n	e	s	d	a	y
l	h	k	g	d	j	q	a	x	d	b	f	n	l	j
d	t	l	s	a	t	u	r	d	a	y	c	r	d	f
t	h	u	u	y	z	z	s	f	y	p	t	n	i	q
s	a	q	n	f	g	t	o	d	a	y	a	m	d	k
f	r	i	d	a	y	p	a	o	k	m	t	l	a	r
g	t	w	a	v	o	s	a	t	t	c	z	f	y	t
u	n	n	y	v	p	o	e	n	o	d	a	y	n	t

☐ Monday

☐ Tuesday

☐ Wednesday

☐ Thursday

☐ Friday

☐ Saturday

☐ Sunday

2

Help Patrick by answering his questions.

a. What day comes after Thursday?

_____

b. How many days are in the week altogether?

_____

c. What day comes before Sunday?

_____

d. How many days are in the weekend?

_____

Telling the Time

SCAN CODE

Mrs. Puff is teaching SpongeBob to tell the time so he is never late for her lesson again! He needs all the boating lessons he can get....

1

Can you answer the questions below?

a. How many minutes are there in an hour? ☐

b. How many hours are there in a day? ☐

2

Draw a line to match these clocks to the correct time.

a.

b.

c.

Half past 4   3 o'clock   6 o'clock

3

SpongeBob knows he needs to be able to read the clock face so he gets to Mrs. Puff's Boating School on time. Draw the hands on these clocks.

a.

b.

c.

Half past 4   Quarter past 7   1 o'clock

d.

e.

f.

3 o'clock   Half past 9   Quarter to 2

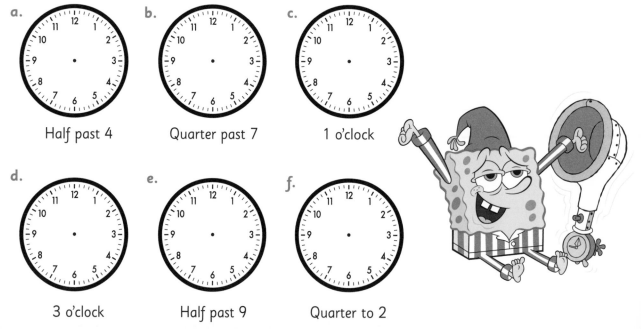

2D Shapes

SpongeBob and his friends all come in different shapes and sizes.

SpongeBob is a rectangle shape.

Patrick is a star shape.

Flat shapes are called 2D shapes.

square   circle   triangle   rectangle   pentagon   hexagon   octagon   oval

1

Match these shapes that SpongeBob has drawn to their names.

a.

b.

c.

d.

pentagon   rectangle   triangle   circle

2

Have a go at labelling these shapes. You can use the shapes at the top of the page to help.

a.

b.

c.

d.

_____ _____ _____ _____

Corners & Sides

SpongeBob is getting ready for ANOTHER boating exam. They haven't gone well so far! He has finally realised that boating signs come in all different 2D shapes and they all mean different things. Perhaps knowing this might help him pass this time!

Different 2D shapes have a different number of sides and corners.

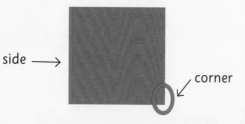

side →

corner ↙

1

Label these shapes with the facts about their sides and corners.

a. ☐ corners ☐ sides

b. ☐ corners ☐ sides

c. ☐ corners ☐ sides

d. ☐ corners ☐ sides

e. ☐ corners ☐ sides

f. ☐ corners ☐ sides

2

SpongeBob is trying to identify the shape names of different boating signs. Help him by matching each description to the correct name.

a. 4 corners and 4 equal sides   Triangle

b. 0 corners and 1 side   Square

c. 3 corners and 3 sides   Circle

3D Shapes

It's SpongeBob's birthday and he's having a party! He has been given lots of presents from his friends and they are all different shapes. These shapes aren't flat; he can pick them up so that means they are 3D shapes.

 cube  cuboid   sphere   cylinder   triangular prism   cone   square-based pyramid

1

Help SpongeBob by naming the shapes.

a. 　　b. 　　c. 　　d.

_____　　_____　　_____　　_____

2

We use special words to describe the properties of 3D shapes.

Vertices is the plural of the word vertex, which is the point at which two or more edges meet. It is another word for corner.

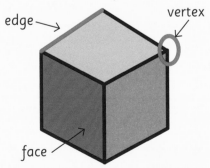

edge

vertex

face

	Number of faces	Number of edges	Number of vertices
a.	☐	☐	☐
b.	☐	☐	☐
c.	☐	☐	☐
d.	☐	☐	☐
e.	☐	☐	☐

3D Shape Nets

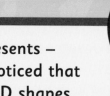

SpongeBob is busy admiring his birthday presents – everyone has been super generous! He has noticed that he can see 2D shapes on the surface of the 3D shapes.

1

He has described some of the things he can see, can you help him by writing the name of the 3D shape?

cube	square-based pyramid	sphere

a. I can see four triangles and a square on this shape.

The shape is a

_____

b. This shape has no 2D shapes that I can see, but when I see its shadow, it is a circle.

The shape is a

_____

c. This shape has six square faces.

The shape is a

_____

2

SpongeBob makes his own 'square pants' each day using a net of the pants and folding it into shape.

a. What is the correct name for the 3D shape that this net makes?

_____

b. What 2D shapes is it made from?

_____

3

SpongeBob has flattened the 3D gift boxes into nets... maybe he is making new pants? Match the nets to the 3D shape that they make.

A shape net shows what a 3D shape looks like if it's opened out flat.

a.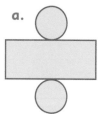

b.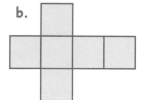

c.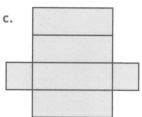

Cuboid	Cylinder	Cube

2D & 3D Shapes

SpongeBob and Patrick have been for a wander all around Bikini Bottom. Looking around, they have found lots of different, interesting shapes. They know that some are 2D and some are 3D, but they don't know which are which!

1

Label the groups of shapes below to say if they are 2D or 3D.

a. We can pick these shapes up. These are _____ shapes.

b. These shapes are flat. We call them _____ shapes.

2

These shapes have got all muddled up! Colour the 2D shapes in red, and the 3D shapes in green.

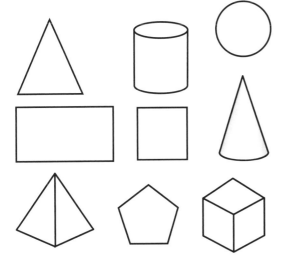

3

SpongeBob and Patrick have tidied the shapes away. Have they done it correctly? Put a circle around the odd ones out.

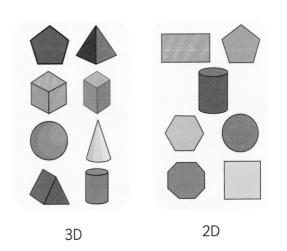

3D   2D

Position

SpongeBob is busy searching for some treasure chests hidden by the ghostly pirate, the Flying Dutchman.

1

Match each picture to the sentence that correctly describes where the treasure is by writing the correct letter in the box.

a.

b.

c.

SpongeBob is **next** to the treasure chest.

SpongeBob is **behind** the treasure chest.

SpongeBob is in **front** of the treasure chest.

2

SpongeBob is so close to finding the treasure! Follow the instructions below to help him mark the locations on the map.

Draw an **X** in the top left square on the map.

Draw an **X** in the bottom right square on the map.

Draw an **X** in the middle square on the map.

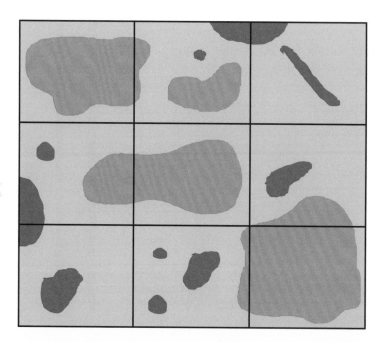

Shape Patterns

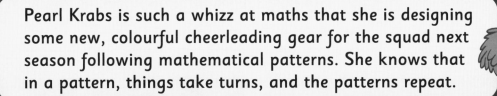

Pearl Krabs is such a whizz at maths that she is designing some new, colourful cheerleading gear for the squad next season following mathematical patterns. She knows that in a pattern, things take turns, and the patterns repeat.

1

Have a go at completing these patterns by colouring in the rest of the boxes.

a.

b.

2

Complete these patterns by drawing the next 2 shapes.

a.

b.

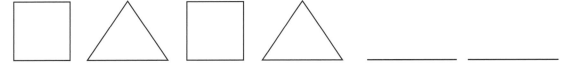

3

Patterns don't always have to be in a line. Pearl is also designing the pom-poms for cheerleading, so she is making circular patterns as well.

Can you help Pearl fill in the missing colours in the pattern on the right?

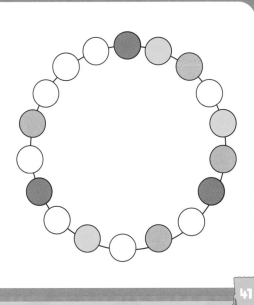

Patterns

Home isn't about barbecues or pecan pies, home is where you're surrounded by critters that care about ya.

Sandy Cheeks is clearing out her Treedome and has found lots of numbered shells from a past sea life maths experiment. She wants to organise them into a pattern as she knows that you can make patterns with numbers as well as shapes and colours.

1

Odd numbers and even numbers are an example of patterns.

Complete these number patterns with odd and even numbers.

a. 2 4 ☐ 8 10 ☐ 14 ☐ 18

b. 5 7 9 ☐ 13 15 ☐ 19 ☐ 23 ☐ 27

2

Patterns can have different jumps between numbers. Have a go at completing these patterns. You need to see how much is added or subtracted between each jump and follow the same rule to find the missing numbers.

a. 3 6 9 12 ☐ 18 21 ☐ 27

b. 40 35 ☐ 25 20 ☐ 10

c. 11 21 31 ☐ 51 61 ☐ 81

3

These patterns are already complete, but can you identify the rule? Look at what is added and subtracted between each step and write it in the box.

a.
☐ ☐ ☐ ☐

4 ⌒ 8 ⌒ 12 ⌒ 16 ⌒ 20

b.
☐ ☐ ☐

83 ⌒ 73 ⌒ 63 ⌒ 53 ⌒ 43

Direction & Movement

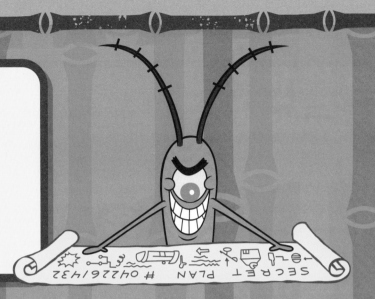

Sheldon J. Plankton will stop at NOTHING to get his hands on the secret formula for making Krabby Patties! Right now, he is trying to sneak into Krusty Krab to steal their recipes, but he needs some directions to follow. Will you help him slink in?

1

Look at the plan that Plankton needs to follow and complete the instructions so he can get to the recipes. The words are in the box to help you.

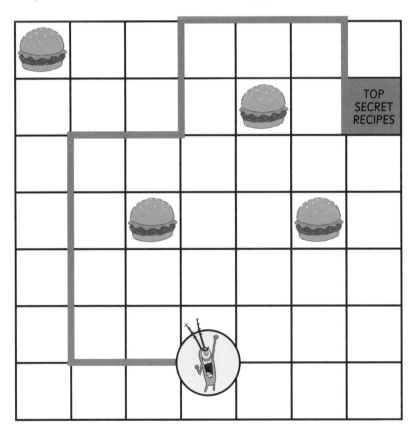

TOP SECRET RECIPES

North

South

East

West

a. Move _____ 2 spaces.

b. Move _____ 4 spaces.

c. Move East _____ spaces.

d. Move North _____ spaces.

e. Move _____ 3 spaces.

f. Move South _____ space.

Pictograms & Tally Charts

Sandy loves being active and on the go. Today, she is extra restless and wants to get moving, but unfortunately, her equipment is all in a muddle!

Help her count how many things she has by making a tally chart. It is really easy to do, just make a vertical mark for the first 4 items that you count, and on the 5th item cross through the 4 lines.

1 2 3 4 **5**

Start again for the 6th item. You might find it helpful to cross the items out as you count them.

1 Sandy had a go at starting this tally chart, can you finish it for her?

	Tally	How many?
(glove)	‖‖‖ ‖‖	8
(skateboard)		
(hockey stick)		
(soccer ball)		
(basketball)		

2 Sandy has started a pictogram to show how many of each piece of equipment she has. Can you use the results from your tally to finish it? Draw the correct number of each item onto the pictogram.

(ball)				
(ball)				
(ball)				
(ball)				
(ball)				
(ball)				
(ball)				
(ball)				
(ball)	(glove)	(hockey stick)	(soccer ball)	(skateboard)

44

Block Charts & Tables

Sweet mother of pearl, it's been a busy day at the Krusty Krab! Mr. Krabs needs your help to count all the food left for tomorrow.

1

For every item you count, colour a box of the block chart in. It might help to cross the items off as you count them. The milkshakes have been counted for you.

2

Mr. Krabs has measured his piles of money and compared them to the piles of money he can see through the window of the Chum Bucket. He's recorded his findings in a table.

	Height at the Krusty Krab	Height at the Chum Bucket
10p coins	20cm	18cm
20p coins	15cm	11cm
£5 notes	36cm	18cm
£10 notes	19cm	17cm

Patrick has taken a sneaky peek at the table and has come up with the statements below. Can you tick whether each one is true or false?

a. All of the piles of money at the Krusty Krab are bigger than at the Chum Bucket. TRUE ☐ FALSE ☐

b. The 20p pile at the Chum Bucket is 7cm shorter than that at the Krusty Krab. TRUE ☐ FALSE ☐

c. The £5 note pile is twice as tall at the Krusty Krab. TRUE ☐ FALSE ☐

Answers

Page 2: Numbers to 100

1.

1	2	3	4	5	6	7	8	9	10
11	12	13	14	15	16	17	18	19	20
21	22	23	24	25	26	27	28	29	30
31	32	33	34	35	36	37	38	39	40
41	42	43	44	45	46	47	48	49	50
51	52	53	54	55	56	57	58	59	60
61	62	63	64	65	66	67	68	69	70
71	72	73	74	75	76	77	78	79	80
81	82	83	84	85	86	87	88	89	90
91	92	93	94	95	96	97	98	99	100

2. a. 19, 28, 37, 48, 60
b. 33, 41, 44, 52, 63, 72
c. 55, 64, 66, 83, 94

Page 3: Counting

1. a. 5   b. 9   c. 12   d. 17
11 - eleven, 4 - four
8 - eight, 19 - nineteen

2. a. 20   c. 7   e. 5
b. 11   d. 2   f. 14

Page 4: Counting

1. a.
b.
c.
d.

2. Completed dot to dot in number order. The picture is Patrick.

Page 5: One more and one less

1. a. One more: 7, One less: 5
b. One more: 5, One less: 3
c. One more: 9, One less: 7
d. One more: 6, One less: 4

2. a. 6   c. 20   e. 15
b. 11   d. 0

Page 6: Comparing numbers

1. 1, 4, 8, 11, 19, 21

2. a. >   b. =   c. <   d. <   e. >

Page 7: Value of digits

1. a. 6 tens and 5 ones
b. 4 tens and 2 ones
c. 3 tens and 8 ones
d. 1 tens and 3 ones
e. 2 tens and 6 ones

2. a. 32   b. 75   c. 49   d. 51   e. 17

3. a. 34   b. 17   c. 25   d. 49

Page 8: Solving number problems

1. a. 13   b. 36   c. 33   d. 39

2. a. True   c. False   e. False
b. False   d. True

Page 9: Adding and taking away to 10

1. a. 8   b. 10   c. 8

2. a. 2   b. 9   c. 4   d. 4

3. a. 3   b. 7   c. 2   d. 4

Page 10: Adding and taking away to 20

1. a. 19   c. 16   e. 1   g. 5
b. 15   d. 12   f. 10   h. 9

2. a. 6 + 4 = 10 so 60 + 40 = 100
b. 2 + 8 = 10 so 20 + 80 = 100
c. 7 + 3 = 10 so 70 + 30 = 100
d. 5 + 5 = 10 so 50 + 50 = 100
e. 1 + 9 = 10 so 10 + 90 = 100

Page 11: Solving addition and subtraction problems

1. a. 10   b. 9   c. 11   d. 12

2. a. 3   b. 6   c. 4   d. 2

Page 12: Addition and subtraction

1. a. 9   b. 25   c. 15   d. 8   e. 9   f. 31

2. a. 12   b. 12   c. 8   d. 7   e. 4   f. 34

Page 13: Addition and subtraction

1. a. 17   c. 19   e. 23   g. 55   i. 63
b. 18   d. 19   f. 56   h. 62   j. 46

Page 14: Part whole models

1. a. 6   b. 6   c. 9   d. 8

2. 19

3. 8

4. 18

Page 15: Finding the inverse

1. a. 3   b. 5   c. 12   d. 13   e. 5

2. a. 12 + 4 = 16, 4 + 12 = 16,
16 - 4 = 12, 16 - 12 = 4
b. 10 + 7 = 17, 7 + 10 = 17,
17 - 7 = 10, 17 - 10 = 7
c. 14 + 6 = 20, 6 + 14 = 20,
20 - 6 = 14, 20 - 14 = 6

Page 16: Grouping and arrays

1. a. 9   b. 10   c. 8   d. 20   e. 20

2. a. 8   b. 9   c. 14   d. 10

Page 17: 2's, 5's and 10's

1. a. 4   b. 10   c. 6   d. 16   e. 8

2. a. 50   b. 35   c. 20   d. 45   e. 15

3. a. 8 x 10 = 80   d. 7 x 10 = 70
b. 2 x 10 = 10   e. 3 x 10 = 30
c. 5 x 10 = 50

Page 18: Odds and evens

1. a. 4, 10, 14, 16, 20
b. 1, 5, 11, 13, 17

2. Odd: 6 and 12
Even: 1, 7 and 11

3. Completed dot to dot in number order.

Page 19: Multiplying and dividing

1. picture a: 4 x 2 = 8, 8 ÷ 2 = 4
picture b: 5 x 5 = 25, 25 ÷ 5 = 5
picture c: 3 x 3 = 9, 9 ÷ 3 = 3
picture d: 7 x 3 = 21, 21 ÷ 3 = 7
picture e: 6 x 3 = 18, 18 ÷ 3 = 6
picture f: 3 x 2 = 6, 6 ÷ 2 = 3
picture g: 3 x 5 = 15, 15 ÷ 5 = 3

Page 20: Multiplying and dividing

1. a. 3 x 4 = 12, 4 x 3 = 12
12 ÷ 4 = 3, 12 ÷ 3 = 4
b. 3 x 6 = 18, 6 x 3 = 18
18 ÷ 6 = 3, 18 ÷ 3 = 6
c. 2 x 10 = 20, 10 x 2 = 20
20 ÷ 10 = 2, 20 ÷ 2 = 10

2. a. 12 ÷ 3 = 4
b. 3 ÷ 1 = 3
c. 21 ÷ 7 = 3

Page 21: Multiplication problems

1. a. 15   c. 40   e. 14   g. 90
b. 100   d. 2   f. 6   h. 25

2. a. 3 x 3 = 9
b. 2 x 4 = 8 or 4 x 2 = 8
c. 4 x 10 = 40 or 10 x 4 = 40
d. 5 x 2 = 10 or 2 x 5 = 10

3. a. 30 minutes
b. 40 fans
c. 18 dumbbells

Page 22: Division problems

1. a. 4   d. 2   g. 5
b. 7   e. 10   h. 9
c. 6   f. 4   i. 3

2. 5

3. 5

4. 10

5. 5

Page 23: Finding a half

1.   **2.**

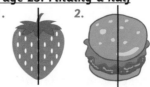

3. a. 2   b. 5   c. 3   d. 6

Page 24: Finding a quarter

1.
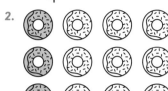

2.
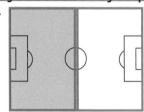

3. a. 2   b. 4   c. 1   d. 3

Page 25: Fractions of shapes

1.
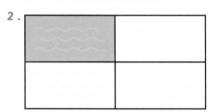

2.
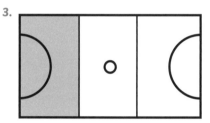

3.
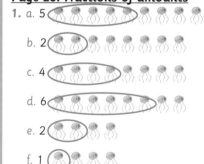

Page 26: Fractions of amounts

1. a. 5

b. 2

c. 4

d. 6

e. 2

f. 1

g. 2

2. a. 3   c. 4   e. 2
   b. 5   d. 8   f. 6

Page 27: Equivalent Fractions

1. a. 2   b. 3

c. 5

d. 8

2.
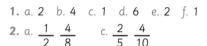

Page 28: Equivalent Fractions

1. a. 2 b. 4 c. 1 d. 6 e. 2 f. 1

2. a. $\frac{1}{2}$ $\frac{4}{8}$ c. $\frac{2}{5}$ $\frac{4}{10}$

b. $\frac{2}{3}$ $\frac{4}{6}$ d. $\frac{1}{4}$ $\frac{3}{12}$

3. a. $\frac{1}{2}$ b. $\frac{1}{4}$ c. $\frac{3}{4}$

Page 29: Measuring

1. a. Shorter   b. Longer

2. a. Shorter   b. Taller

3. a. Lighter   b. Heavier

Page 30: Comparing Measurements

1. 9cm   2. 6cm

3. The Kelp Bar is longer

4. a. 100g   b. 400g   c. Yes

Page 31: Money

1. 1, d
   2, a
   3, b
   4, c

2. a. 85p   b. 70p   c. 95p

Page 32: Ordering events in a day

1.

2. a. Wake up - morning
   b. Jelly fishing with Patrick - afternoon
   c. Go to sleep - evening

Page 33: Days of the week

1.
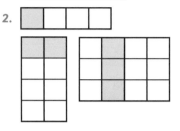

2. a. Friday   c. Saturday
   b. 7   d. 2

Page 34: Telling the time

1. a. 60   b. 24

2. a. 6 o'clock   c. 3 o'clock
   b. Half past 4

3. a.   d.
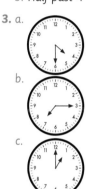
   b.   e.

   c.   f.
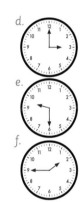

Page 35: 2D Shapes

1. a. circle   c. rectangle
   b. triangle   d. pentagon

2. a. square   c. hexagon
   b. oval   d. octagon

Page 36: 2D Shapes Corners and Sides

1. a. 3 corners, 3 sides
   b. 4 corners, 4 sides
   c. 8 corners, 8 sides
   d. 5 corners, 5 sides
   e. 0 corners, 1 sides
   f. 4 corners, 4 sides

2. a. square   b. circle   c. triangle

Page 37: 3D Shapes

1. a. sphere   c. cuboid
   b. cube   d. cylinder

2. a. 6 faces, 12 edges, 8 vertices
   b. 1 faces, 0 edges, 0 vertices
   c. 6 faces, 12 edges, 8 vertices
   d. 3 faces, 2 edges, 0 vertices
   e. 2 faces, 1 edges, 1 vertex

Page 38: 3D Shape nets

1. a. square-based pyramid
   b. sphere
   c. cube

2. a. cuboid   b. rectangles

3. a. cylinder   b. cube   c. cuboid

Page 39: Identifying 2D and 3D shapes

1. a. 3D b. 2D

2.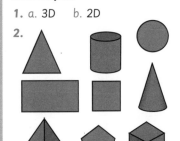

3.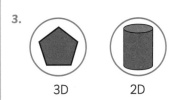

3D   2D

Page 40: Positions

1. a. SpongeBob is in front of the treasure chest.
   b. SpongeBob is behind the treasure chest.
   c. SpongeBob is next to the treasure.

2.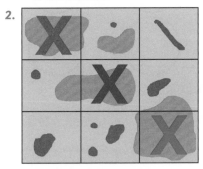

Page 41: Shape patterns

1. a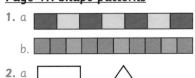
   b.

2. a
   b.

3.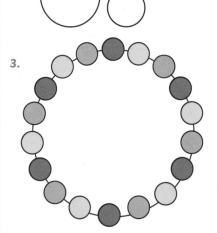

Page 42: Patterns

1. a. 6, 12, 16   b. 11, 17, 21, 25

2. a. 15, 24   b. 30, 15   c. 41, 71

3. a. + 4, + 4. + 4, + 4
   b. −10, −10, −10, −10

Page 43: Direction and movement

1. a. Move West 2 spaces.
   b. Move North 4 spaces.
   c. Move East 2 spaces.
   d. Move North 2 spaces.
   e. Move East 3 spaces.
   f. Move South 1 space.

Page 44: Pictograms and tally charts

1.

	Tally	How many?
🧤	⊞⊞ III	8
🛹	II	2
hockey stick	⊞⊞	5
⚽	III	3
⚪	⊞⊞ III	8

2.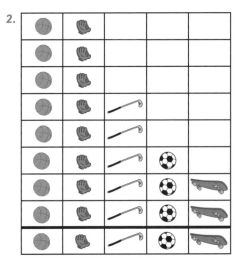

Page 45: Block charts and tables

1.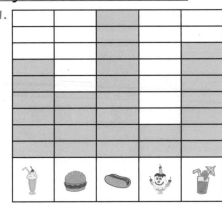

2. a. True   b. False   c. True

48